AR WARS™

Han Solo

Reed Children's Books

Who is Han Solo?

Han Solo is a smuggler from the
Corellia star system. Han is captain of the
Millennium Falcon. His first mate is Chewbacca,
a Wookiee from the jungle planet of Kashyyyk.

s content to make money whenever he can
oting the *Falcon* on smuggling missions…
e meets Luke Skywalker and joins the
struggle against the evil Empire.

As a smuggler, Han deals with members of the galaxy's criminal underworld. During one mission, he loses some cargo which belongs to Jabba the Hutt, one of the most powerful gangsters in the galaxy.

ng an enemy of Jabba the Hutt is extrem
gerous. Jabba offers a reward to anyone
can deliver Han to him. From this mome
Han is prey for bounty hunters all over
galaxy.

Millennium Falcon

Millennium Falcon is a Corellian freighter. Rebuilt by Han Solo and his old friend Lando Calrissian, the *Falcon* has a lot of speed and firepower. A smuggler's ship, the *Falcon* also has a secret underfloor compartment. Han, Luke, Ben, and Chewie hide there when the ship is searched by stormtroopers.

Han boasts that the *Millennium Falcon* can out-fly almost any other ship. When Lando leads the Rebel attack on the second Death Star, Han lends him the *Falcon*. The *Falcon* once belonged to Lando, but Han won her from him in a card game.

Han meets Luke and Ben in the Mos Eisley
Cantina on Tatooine. They need to deliver a
message from the Rebel leader, Princess Leia,
who has been captured by Darth Vader. Han
agrees to take them - for a price. Luke
persuades Han to help him rescue the Princess.

Han becomes involved with the Rebels' struggle. He joins the battle to destroy Death Star and is honoured by Princess for his bravery. From this moment on, H yal member of the Rebel Alliance.

s older than Luke and regards him as
erienced kid when they first meet.
ually, Han is won over by Luke's coura
etermination. They become life-long fr

Han and Chewie Chewbacca is Han's first mate on the *Millennium Falcon*. When Han gives up smuggling to join the Rebel Alliance, Chewie goes with him. Han and Chewie are totally loyal to each other and make a great team.

When Han first meets Leia, he is not prepared for her tough, no-nonsense attitude. Both have strong personalities and they clash from the

Han and Leia have to depend on each other in many dangerous situations as they battle against the Empire. They learn to trust each other and become friends. Eventually, their friendship turns to love.

en the Rebel base on Hoth is discovered he Empire, Luke escapes to Dagobah. Ha wie, and Leia take refuge on the planet pin, which is governed by Lando Calrissia ortunately for Han, Darth Vader has arriv and has forced Lando to betray his frien

Han and his friends are captured by Vader. Lando helps Leia and Chewie to escape, but they cannot save Han. Frozen in carbonite, he is turned over to the bounty hunter Boba Fett. Fett delivers Han to his old enemy, Jabba the Hutt.

Han's situation seems desperate. Frozen, he hangs on the wall of Jabba's palace in the Tatooine desert. But his friends have not forgotten him. Together, they plan his rescue.

Disguised as a bounty hunter with Chewbacca posing as her prisoner, Leia enters Jabba's palace. She unfreezes Han and, with help from Luke and Lando, they make a daring escape.

rns to
l base, but there is not a
to lose. The Empire has built a second
ar. The space station is protected by
y field generated from the nearby moon
Han volunteers to lead an expedition to
shut down the generator.

On Endor, the Rebels are surprised by stormtroopers. There is a terrible battle outside the generator bunker, but Chewie captures an Imperial scout walker. Thinking quickly, Han uses the walker's radio to trick the stormtroopers into opening the doors.

The Rebels rush into the bunker and blow up the
generator just in time. The Death Star's energy
shield goes down, and the Rebel fighters attack.
As the space station explodes in the sky above
Endor, Han knows that the struggle is over. He
and his friends have won!